Let's Be Friends Again!

By the same author, and available in Picture Knight

I'LL ALWAYS LOVE YOU

Let's Be Friends Again!

By HANS WILHELM

Picture Knight

British Library Cataloguing in Publication Data

Wilhelm, Hans
   Let's be friends again!
   I. Title
  813'.54[J]   PZ7

   ISBN 0-340-42132-0

Text and illustrations copyright © Hans Wilhelm, Inc. 1986

First published 1986 by Crown Publishers, Inc., New York
First published in Great Britain 1986 by Hodder and Stoughton Children's Books
This edition first published 1988 by Picture Knight
Second impression 1988

Published by Hodder and Stoughton Paperbacks,
a division of Hodder and Stoughton Ltd,
Mill Road, Dunton Green, Sevenoaks, Kent TN13 2YE
Editorial office: 47 Bedford Square, London WC1B 3DP

Printed in Belgium by Proost International Book Production

This is a story about my little sister and me.

Usually we got along well together. But ... sometimes my little sister was a real pest. Particularly when I had to baby-sit.

But she was a good listener
when I told bedtime stories.

Sometimes I hated
having to share things
with her all the time.

But she was a great pirate!

One day my little sister did a terrible thing.

She thought that my pet turtle needed more exercise.

So she decided to set it free in the pond!

When I saw what she had done, I was crosser than I'd ever been before.

Now she was going to get it from me.

But my parents didn't like that idea and separated us quickly.

My sister said that she was sorry.
But I felt that was not enough!
I was very angry.

She even offered to buy me a new turtle
with her pocket money. But I didn't want a new one.
I wanted MY turtle back!

My parents didn't say much. They
seemed to be on her side. I went
to my room and slammed the
door as loudly as I could.

I thought of many ways to punish my little sister.

I tried to get some sleep.

But it didn't work.

I began to feel sick. I was convinced
I even had a temperature!

I was too upset to get out of bed. Meanwhile, my sister was singing and dancing in the garden. She seemed to be having the best time of her life.

I was the one who was upset and my little sister didn't seem to care at all. My turtle was gone! How could she forget all about it so easily. I was cross, cross, CROSS!

I punched my pillows
a few times as hard as I could,
let go of an awful scream...

and felt a lot better.

Finally I knew what to do.

I got up and put on my shoes.

Then I went outside to where my sister was feeding the dog.

I said to her, "I'll help you with that," and she smiled.

"By the way," I said after a little while, "the thing with the turtle is OK. I'm not angry anymore."

"Does that mean we are friends again?" asked my sister.

"Yes," I said. "We're friends again."

I was surprised how easy it was to say that. Then I asked her, "Do you want to come to the pet shop with me?"

"To buy a new turtle?"

"No," I said and smiled.

"We are going to buy a couple of hamsters,"
I said. "One for you and one for me. We can
keep them in the old aquarium."

My sister took my hand and off we went.

PRINTED IN BELGIUM BY

proost

INTERNATIONAL BOOK PRODUCTION